THE HORSE'S FOOT AND RELATED PROBLEMS

A practical guide for owners, Farriers and Vets

Robbie C Richardson RSS

Published by:-
Greatcombe Clinic,
Holne,
Devon,
TQ13 7SP

Contents

ACKNOWLEDGMENTS

In preparing this book I would like to thank the following:

NR Pierce, BA, DCR, FRSH, MI Diag H, for his work in radiology.

William Watts and his father, Bill Watts, FWCFs, for being two of the best college teachers that any student could wish for.

Richard Parsons for his work with the equine diet and his unending patience when sharing his knowledge with me.

Nathan Shezall for the digital execution of my line drawings.

Rosie – for still being with us!

And, last but not least, Frank and Glad for teaching me how to learn.

Preface

Greatcombe Clinic is dedicated to the horse. It was opened because of a necessity to provide facilities for surgical shoeing in an environment that was specifically designed for that purpose. There are significant advantages in offering facilities in which to keep and treat a horse, without incurring the inescapable problems associated with the environmental conditions that can exist elsewhere.

The Clinic also concerns itself to a large degree with the general diet of the horse. It is quite common to find that many foot problems start with what the horse is eating. This is not only true for laminitics but also for many animals that show signs of foot trouble, for instance young stock, show horses, etc.

Through the many courses that are run at the Clinic it is possible to spread the word about foot balance, dietary advice, etc., but when I discovered that none of the colleges were covering my particular approach to Farriery, I decided to write a book for the benefit of the owner, Farrier and Vet, and to include, in simple terminology, the conclusions I have reached through my years of shoeing horses.

Let me say at the outset, that I believe I have learned more through my mistakes than my successes, since if you get something right first time it is tempting to assume that it was because of your skill. Whereas if you get something wrong, you then have to work out how to put it right, and hence store the knowledge for future reference.

The purpose of this book is to offer help to those who want some new and some old ways of dealing with equine problems. All the recommendations in this book are a result of work carried out at the Clinic.

In time, I hope that every good Farrier is encouraged through the strength of his own convictions to write a book. In this way it will enable all Farriers to understand just what changes and innovations are taking place, and how to cope with the increasing demands put upon their profession, which, far from being static is, in fact, ever changing.

PROFESSIONAL ETIQUETTE

Professional etiquette is the respect due to one professional by another.

If this does not exist, then there is no professionalism.

Consulting between professionals should be done direct, and not through a third party.

— 1 —
The Team

T he team that is created in order for the owner to enjoy a sound and happy horse always has certain essential elements. It must, I believe, contain the following:

1) The Veterinary Surgeon (Team Leader)
2) The Farrier
3) The Dietician
4) The Saddler.

This list can, of course, be added to according to the specific needs of the animal. The job of the owner is to seek a Vet who will form such a team. Sadly, all too often I have come across a group of professionals that do not communicate between each other.

In the Professional World of riding and competition there is always a team who communicate in order for the horse to be given the best chance, whether it be racing, jumping, dressage etc, and is there really any marked difference between the professional owner and the leisure owner?

The Vet must organise a team from people that he/she can work with. It is totally self-defeating to have a Farrier that will not talk to the Vet and vice-versa. As a result of the Animal Welfare Act, a Vet is the individual in whose charge the well being of the animal ultimately rests, and is therefore in a position of delegation. Although there are Farriers who may find this distasteful, I believe that in time the good Vet will work with the good Farrier, looking after the good horse for the good owner.

During the work that I have done with many different types of horses and ponies, I am becoming increasingly aware of the important effect that feeding has upon the animal, and that is why it is essential that a Dietician is included in the team. Most Vets that I have worked with take a similar view.

The Saddler has a degree of responsibility with regard the general soundness of the animal as it is often the case that a badly fitting saddle will convert the animal's gait into that of a lame horse.

I believe that once this TEAM has been formed, it is then the responsibility of that Team to keep the animal sound. This is done by any one of the Team informing the others when something untoward is detected. There is no doubt that the horse will benefit, and what is more, when we have put a Team together, the owner has found that the overall costs of keeping the horse are no more than when it was being looked after by a group of individuals, but the general well-being of the animal has increased significantly.

People have talked a lot about the need for 'owner-education'. This I think is a sad reflection on our respective professions. Just as I do not wish to fathom the finer points about plumbing in order to recognise whether I have a good plumber, neither should the owner take on the responsibility of comprehending the finer points of these respective professions in order to know whether he/she has picked a good team. The owner can, of course, still pursue his/her own interests in whatever field they wish. However, I feel that ultimately the Team should be strong enough to dictate policy to the owner, even if the joint professional opinions differ from theirs. If this advice is not taken then there is a breakdown in communications and it is then the job of the Vet, after discussion with the rest of the team, to put over the case, and the job of the other professionals to back him/her up. I can say through experience that a good team always gets along with the owner and achieves great results!

The owner has the job of finding a good Vet. This can be achieved by asking any other members of the team, or anyone who is respected in the horse world, who they would recommend to treat a horse. Only a Vet who has the respect of other professionals will be able to form an efficient equine team.

Finally, it is an added bonus if the team has a good back-up system of Consultants, so that each member will know of someone they can call upon to obtain further advice should it be needed. This is by no means an admission of ignorance, but rather the confirmation of intelligence.

A GOOD TEAM MAKES A GREAT HORSE!

2

Anatomy

The detail in this section will be very basic and therefore hopefully easy to understand. It is important that we communicate using a common language that we all agree upon. Vets tend to talk about anatomy more with owners than they do with Farriers, and use more familiar terminology, so for the purposes of this book I will do the same.

Glossary of terminology:-

Acute	short sharp pain
Anterior	front
Artery	vessel that takes oxygenated blood away from the heart
Atrophy	wasting tissue
Axis	line through the middle i.e. of a joint
Bursa	a bag containing synovia, acting as a buffer between tendon, bone, ligament, joints etc.
Capillary	small blood vessels at the end of arteries and veins.
Carpus	the knee joint of the horse
Cartilage	a white, smooth, plastic like material covering the articulation area of the bone
Caudal	back, part nearest the rear of the animal
Chronic	persisting pain, as opposed to acute
Collateral	being at the side
Congenital	from birth
Corium	inner layer of skin carrying nerves, a lot of blood and the protective skin oil
Degeneration	change for the worse
Distal	point furthest away from centre or attachment
Dorsal	the forward-most point on the wall of the horse's foot
Dumped	foot taken back beyond correct pastern/foot axis
Epidermis	outside layer of skin that does not carry blood
Exostosis	a bone growth protruding from the normal
Extension	making a joint go forward, extension tendons are at the front of a leg
Flexion	making a joint retreat i.e. picking up a foot. Flexion tendons are at the back of a leg

Foramen	Openings for blood vessels, nerves etc to pass through
Hypertrophy	tissue or cells getting larger
Inferior	lower
Inflammation	swelling or heat due to activity, often some loss of function
Lateral	at the side
Lesion	damage to tissue by disease or injury
Malignant	very virulent or infectious tissue
Medial	towards the middle
Ossification	the conversion or forming of bone
Papilla	in the foot, the corium papilla are the small projections in the centre of each horn tubule
Periosteum	skin of the bone, also helps to form bone
Phalanx	bones found in fingers and toes. In a horse found from the fetlock down.
Plexus	a collection of blood or nerve supplies
Posterior	at the back
Protein	made from a variety of amino acids, very important in the structure of all living things.
Proximal	closest to the point of reference
Plantar	referring to the sole surface of the foot
Rarefaction	bone becoming less dense
Radiology	x-rays
Seating-out	making sure a shoe is not bearing on the sole
Sesamoid	the two small bones behind the fetlock
Superior	above
Superficial	nearest the surface
Synovia	a clear, oil-like liquid that is found in joints
Tarsus	in the horse this means hock
Tendinitis	inflammation of the tendon
Vein	the vessel which takes the blood back to the heart
Vaulted	when the sole is very deep, or hollow

I would like to single out one piece of anatomy for special attention – the frog.

I have found the frog and connection tissue to be one of the most important parts of the horse. When we talk of horse balance, I believe that this is where is all starts. Inside the frog there is the frog stay. This will bio-mechanically react to any changes that may happen to the foot either through the horse's natural action or through shoeing.

The frog stay will bend in any direction in order to try and maintain and centralise the foot to the action of the animal. If you keep the frog well trimmed then any change that takes place will show up straight away. Do not allow the frog to get overgrown as this will lead to undue pressure being directed to areas it should not. The size of frog is very important. If the horse has a big frog then it usually means that the animal is trying to relieve the horn of some weight, and you must find out why.

Small frogs can mean that they are not getting enough work, and that the circulation is being impeded somehow, and as a result frog tissue is not being produced. Remember controlled concussion is a good thing and serves to stimulate growth.

Fig 1 – Foot viewed from the back

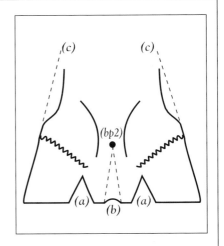

(a) sulcus: The groove that goes down each side of the frog.

(b) frog cleft: This is a depression found in the middle and towards the back of the frog. The centre of this depression has an internal attachment called the frog stay, the top of which I call **Balance Point 2 (BP2).**

I believe **BP2** to be very important when it comes to balancing a foot.

It should be on the same line as **BP1**, which is the point where (c) and (c) cross. If ever you come across a foot where the frog is leaning to one side, you will find that it is trying to place itself under BP1.

Those who wish to study anatomy in greater detail may like to know some of the books and videos I recommend:-

Books

1. *Adams lameness in Horses.* Ted S. Stashak
2. *Shoeing For Performance.* Haydon Price and Rod Fisher
3. *The Lame Horse.* Dr. James R. Rooney
4. *The Mechanics of the Horse.* Dr. James R. Rooney
5. *The Principles of Horseshoeing* (11) Dr. Doug Butler
6. *Veterinary Notes for Horse Owners.* Capt. M. Horace Hayes FRCVS (diet)
7. *Laminitis and its prevention.* R. Eustace

Videos

1. *The Vascular Process of the Equine Limb.* Dr. C. Pollit
2. *Radiography.* P. Webbon
3. *Horses in Motion.* J. Grandage

Knowing anatomy by name is a very small part of understanding the horse. In fact, it is essential to understand the bio-mechanics of the animal and I would always choose to work with a person who knows how the animal works, above the one who can name all the parts correctly. There are books that go into this in great detail, one of which I have mentioned; *The Mechanics of the Horse* by Dr. James R. Rooney.

Fig 2 – Bones below the knee

1 = M3	Large metacarpal or cannon bone.
2 = M2 and M4	Splint bones or small metacarpals.
3 =	Proximal sesamoids.(2)
4 = P1	Long pastern, proximal phalanx.
5 = P2	Short pastern, middle phalanx.
6 = P3	Pedal, coffin bone, distal phalanx.
7 =	Distal sesamoid, Navicular bone.

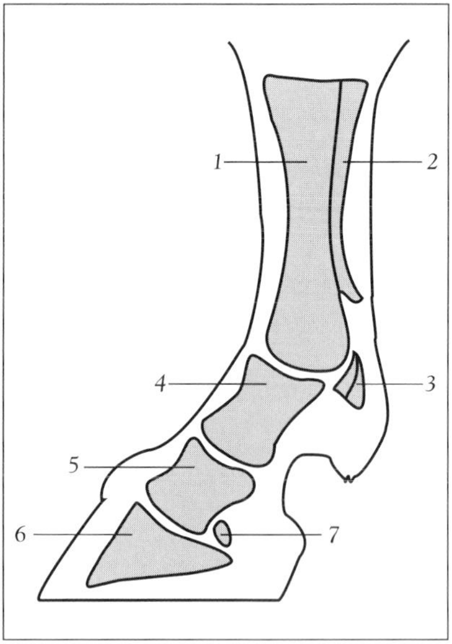

I consider it particularly important to spend some time looking at SOUND horses and not always assessing LAME horses. Often Farriers are asked to look at a horse that is lame, without really knowing the true movement of the animal. Is it just compensating for muscle loss? Is it sound in its legs but hurting elsewhere?

These factors and many others besides can only be correctly judged if you have a thorough knowledge and understanding of the movement of the horse.

The Horse's Foot and Related Problems

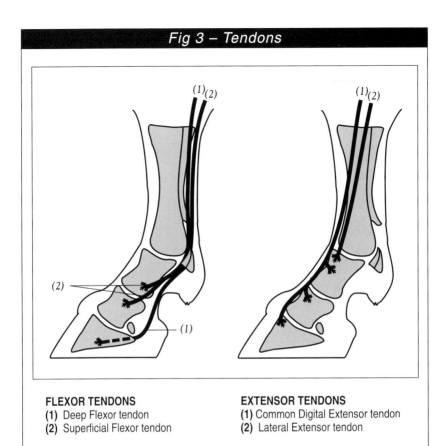

Fig 3 – Tendons

FLEXOR TENDONS
(1) Deep Flexor tendon
(2) Superficial Flexor tendon

EXTENSOR TENDONS
(1) Common Digital Extensor tendon
(2) Lateral Extensor tendon

Go to an Endurance Ride, because at these events there are a lot of horses being assessed as to their soundness. Make your own notes, and ask the adjudicating Vet and Farrier for help. Build up you own folder on action and keep it for future reference. It will prove invaluable. How does the action of a cob compare to that of a thoroughbred for instance?

Why have some horses got one shoulder at a different angle to the other? Is it because the foot is out of balance? Why do most horses have a larger muscle mass on one shoulder? How does this show itself in the saddle?

It was only when I started to do this exercise that I began to truly understand my profession, and the notes that I made then, I still refer to and find useful today.

Fig 4 – Foot: Saggital section

(a) Wall
(b) horny laminae
(c) sensitive laminae
(d) laminae corium
(e) digital cushion
(f) sole
(g) sensitive sole
(h) frog
(i) Sensitive frog
(j) lateral cartilage

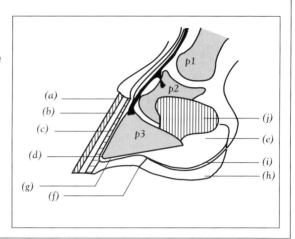

BLOOD

The blood supply to the foot of a horse is crucial in two ways.

Firstly, good healthy blood feeds all the relevant parts of the foot and therefore if the blood changes in any way this will manifest itself by producing a ring on the wall of the foot. Some of these rings are only visible

Fig 5 – Blood supply

Every part of the foot needs feeding with blood.This figure shows the main areas supplied by the common digital artery

Blood is pumped to the areas by the heart. It is then taken back to the heart by veins.

The vein has no muscle spasm of its own, or help from the heart, so it relies on a mechanical method of return achieved by effective use of concussion and non-return valves within the vein itself.

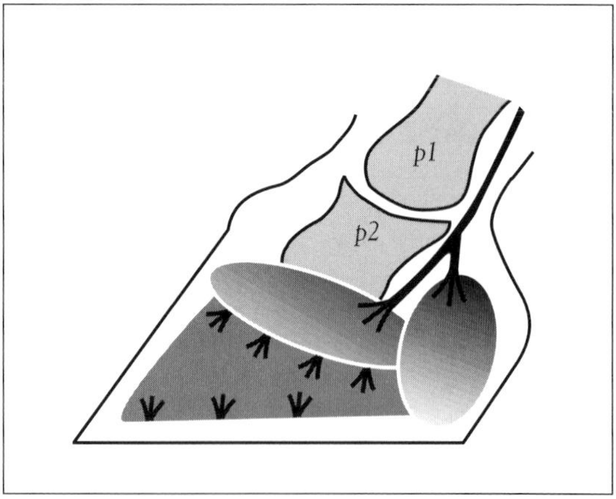

under magnification, others, such as those brought about by a change of diet, lameness, shock or coming into work after a period of rest, will be very obvious. These rings can lead to the wall being out of line with the bone inside (P3) and thus causing stress on the hoof capsule.

It is most important that the blood supply is not diminished in any area. This is a very common complaint, and these feet are often out of balance. It means that the growth of the wall can be inconsistent and lead to added strain being placed on the weaker parts of the wall. One of the principal areas of blood supply is at the caudal part of the foot and it is this area that must be supported when shoeing.

This leads on to the second crucial point. The blood supply mechanism is a liquid shock absorber and the ability of the animal to move freely will largely depend on how efficiently this shock absorber is working.

LIGAMENTS

Ligaments tie bones together, keep tendons in place, or encase a joint. They are very strong, and if badly damaged, will often cause the ruin of a horse.

If a horse is out of balance there is a good chance that a ligament will be trying to resist the strain of this imbalance and will create a compromise in order for the animal to survive.

Although this section does not go into great detail, all the parts of anatomy mentioned would be those effected if the horse had a natural or man-made conformation defect. When considering a possible cure, cause and effect must be taken into account. In other words if a shoe is fitted in order to correct a problem that is only in the foot, it could have an adverse effect somewhere else in the animal. If this is at all likely then it must be taken into account.

YOUR NOTES

The Horse's Foot and Related Problems

——— 3 ———
Balance

The Penguin English Dictionary describes balance as being: *harmony between parts of a whole*, and that is how I would like to use the word when talking about the balance of horse and rider.

First I think it is essential to find out if the rider is aware of any imbalance that they themselves may have. This can be achieved by perhaps going to a Chiropractor or Osteopath and asking them for an assessment. If anything should be found that is likely to cause a deviation in your gait, then this would in turn have to be taken into account when fitting saddles, riding or doing anything that may involve the horse having to compromise in its action.

One thing that you can do at home to establish whether you are out of balance in either the sitting or the standing position is to get two bathroom scales and place them head to head about three inches apart, then stand on them with either foot in the centre of each one. Extend your arms out to the side about a foot away from your body, keep your head up and get a friend to take both readings.

You can also place the scales in a similar way on a table and sit with one buttock on each scale and read your weight distribution at the sitting position. We have recorded as much as a three stone discrepancy between the scales on a twelve and a half stone person! Imagine what that must do to the saddle, back, muscles, legs, feet, shoe-wear, and ultimately, the performance of your horse.

If you wish to know more about this type of self-assessment, I would recommend reading a paper by Dr Bernard Masters entitled – *Bodysense*.

Once the rider is deemed to be balanced then we can turn to the animal. The individual members of the Team will each have their own theories as to the balance of the horse, and from a Farrier's point of view, I know that unless we all talk to each other on the subject, no one member can hope to reach a successful conclusion on their own.

The eye, once trained, is probably the best judge of balance. Untrained it will usually ignore any defect and compromise by resorting to tradition or habit. By this I mean that if someone has been taught to do something in a way that creates an imbalance, and finds that method easier, then the eye will accept that as the norm. This, I think, is the biggest cause of imperfection in my profession.

Fig 6 – Balancing the Foot by Eye

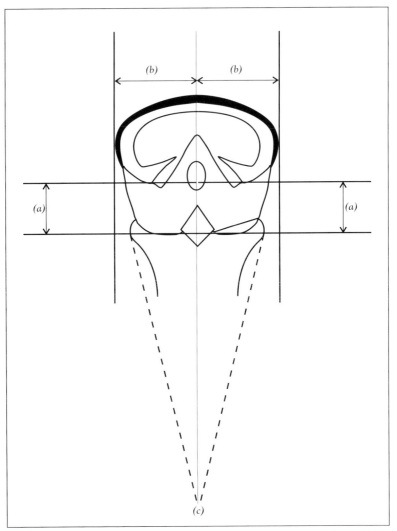

This is a position in which you will often see the foot and it is a good angle from which to assess balance. Are the heels the same length? **(a)** Is the distance from the centre of the frog to the outside of the foot the same on both sides? **(b)** (Especially in the hind feet!)

Is the angle of the wall each side of the foot the same? In other words, if you were to draw a line up each side of the foot, would they meet in the centre of the leg? **(c)** This I have called Balance Point 1. **(BP1.)**

The Horse's Foot and Related Problems

Fig 7 – Balancing the Foot by Eye

Viewing the foot from the front while it is on the ground.
In this position you can also look for relevant angles and references.
(a) and (b) should be the same.
(g) and (h) should be the same.
Angles (e) and (f) should be the same.
If a line were to be drawn up from each side of the foot it should meet in the centre on the leg at reference point (i) **(BP1)**

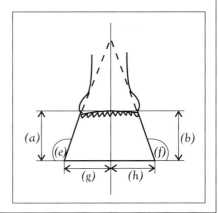

Fig 8 – Balancing the Foot by Eye

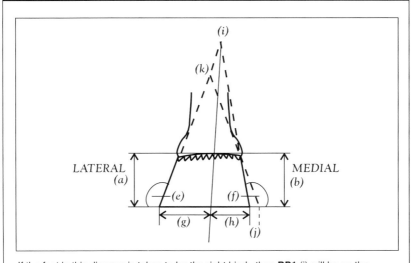

If the foot in this diagram is taken to be the right hind, then **BP1** (i) will be on the inside. This will lead to strain on the outside of the leg, and in the case of the fetlock, can result in windgalls.

The way to balance this foot is first to make sure that (g) and (h) are the same width, even if this means extending the shoe on the inside, (j) for although the inside heel may be high, the lateral and medial wall could be the same length. This means that angle (f) is too upright. By taking this action the **BP1** (k) will move to the centre, thus starting the balancing process. The height of **BP1** will differ from breed to breed. The more upright the foot the higher **BP1** will be.

Fig 9 – Reference points

This shows a horse viewed from the front, with reference points for the owner, Farrier and Vet to use.
I find it a very useful guide when looking at a horse on behalf of the client who may be a prospective buyer.
When looking at young horses, remember these measurements can alter a great deal.

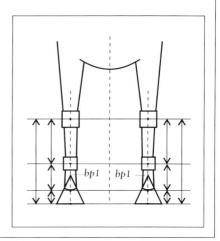

Fig 10 – Balance of the rider

Here we see the rider sitting on the horse in a balanced position.
Although it is not possible to see yourself on a horse without the aid of a large mirror, I do recommend that you ask someone to stand in front of you while you are mounted, and draw imaginary lines through your body as shown in the diagram.
(a) through the hips
(b) through the knees
(c) through the foot or ankle
(d) a centre line from the top of the rider's head to the centre of the horse's chest.

If even one of these lines is not straight then you will find that the others will also be off, and this in turn will make the horse unbalanced.

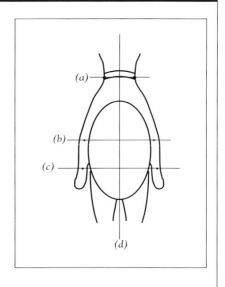

For the owner to be able to judge whether a horse is balanced or not, involves great natural skill. Although you can train your eye to a certain degree, in the final analysis it is an un-explainable phenomenon. How often have you looked at a horse and judged it to be a mechanical disaster that would not be able to negotiate an open gate, let alone the open ditch, and yet later you see the same animal later performing to perfection?

In order to help to train yourself and your eye, go to a good yard and watch the professionals riding good horses around the school. Try and judge for yourself why this is a good horse and why the rider is better than you. It is so easy to just stand and admire without actually learning something.

In the Dressage world, balance is something that you are actually judged upon, so not only is it important to be balanced for comfort, but it is also beneficial to your progress in many of the equine disciplines.

Fig 10 provides a simple diagram to show balance.

One of the more common problems that I come across concerning balance is a well balanced foot on an unbalanced leg. This suggests to me that the farrier has not seen the horse in motion and has therefore assumed that the horse will move in accordance to the way it has been shod. If this is the case, then the balanced foot will in fact cause the overall imbalance of the animal to deteriorate leading to a worsening in its movement.

When I assess a horse I am usually able to tell the owner how it moves simply by looking at its foot stance. But it would be too complacent to go ahead and shoe the animal without first watching it walk and/or trot up.

When dealing with what I call "Fine Tuning" (i.e. the top class dressage horse that is just missing the prize money because of small conformation defects) then it often pays to have another rider put the horse through its paces so that the owner, together with the Team, can assess any slight defects in conformation from ground level. Videos at this stage are very useful. In fact I would always recommend a buyer to take a video of the horse at the time of purchase in order to keep a record of the animal's development.

Balance is about understanding the whole animal. If it is merely not feeling well, it may show up in its conformation, and no shoeing in the world will make it right, but the Team as a group can!

A final thought on the subject of balance:

When a horse is born it does its best, in conjunction with nature, to balance itself.
When man interferes, nature no longer controls the balance.
The more we understand nature's aims, the more we can assist the horse to cope with the interventions of man.
This is the dilemma between performance and perfection.

The Horse's Foot and Related Problems

— 4 —
Shoeing – Basic & Surgical

Basic shoeing is the term I will use for the usual job that is practiced everyday by Farriers. They tend to travel to the horse, put on the shoes that have been requested, charge for the job done, and leave. For this job to be done well there are one or two procedures that have to be carried out by both the owner and the Farrier.

First, the owner must make sure that the horse is presented to the Farrier in a

> well lit,
> hard,
> level and
> clean environment.

The owner, or representative of, must be present while the horse is being shod.

Second, the Farrier should study the horse that he/she is going to shoe.

I find that a good way of doing this is to watch the horse move on a level surface, and it may even pay to make notes as to the animal's action, because if there are a mass of deviations that could cause problems, it is often hard to remember them all. The owner will also become aware of what you are trying to achieve. If, as a Farrier, I think that there is a deviation that could cause problems, then I always ask for the name of the Vet and discuss possible treatments with him/her before continuing. I would give this standard of attention to every horse I shoe regardless of value, breed or work load.

When it comes to the act of shoeing a horse, I find that no matter how someone has been trained, there is always an independent input that arises simply due to the fact that the Farrier is an individual. This must be taken in account when observing a horse. I have found that some Farriers will be much happier shoeing certain types of horses than anothers. For instance a Farrier who mainly shoes in racing yards would not necessarily want to know the finer points of shire shoeing and vice versa.

This is very common and accepted in the Veterinary profession. A small animal Vet would not attempt to perform a complex equine operation without referring, or consulting a specialist. We are particularly lucky in this country as in any one area a Farrier is likely to come across all types of horses and ponies to be shod, and therefore has the chance to shoe for all types of equine performance.

When shoeing, a horse's foot should be balanced with the whole animal and supported.

Helpful hints

• Before you see a horse, do not have a preconceived idea of what angle the foot should be. You may have to work towards the correct angle gradually.

Fig 11 – Domed Wall

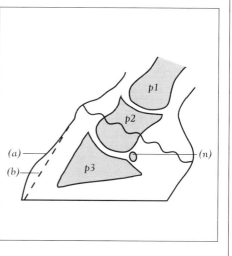

This foot shows a dome on the dorsal wall (a).
This is usually caused by not dressing the foot (b) before the shoe is attached.
The dome will always be in line with the exit of the nails from the hoof wall.
This type of foot is quite a common sight, and it is of no advantage to the horse at all, in fact in bad cases the horse will not be extending as well as it might.
In many cases you will also notice that the foot will be cracked from the dome down to the ground surface, usually on the medial or lateral aspect.

• I always dress the foot forward before putting the shoe on. This stops a curve appearing on the wall's surface, and strain at the point of the nail exit due to the deviation of constant ground pressure. (fig.11)

• I roll the toes of all my shoes, but not the foot. I find that this makes the shoes last a lot longer, and improves the action of the horse. (fig12)

• I use the least amount of nails necessary in a shoe, quite often just four. This reduces the strain between the shoe and the foot. Two clips on the front shoe are often better than more nails.

The Horse's Foot and Related Problems

Fig 12 – Normal Foot

This figure shows a normal foot. Note the support at the heel. I use side clips on both front and hind shoes because, when shoeing a good foot, this enables me to use a lot less nails, due to less medial lateral forces exerted on the shoe.
The toe of the shoe is always rolled, not the foot.

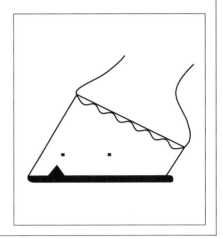

• Do not be afraid of change, but don't change for change's sake.

Basic shoeing is where it all starts. If a good Farrier is faced with quality feet, then it is usually the case that the feet will stay in the same condition. The problem comes when either, the feet have an un-identified defect, or, the Farrier finds the feet are altering due to the way the horse is being shod.

Receiving the right treatment from the right team, a normal working horse should be free of the following common problems:-

a) Cracked feet
b) Most types of Flat feet
c) Corns
d) Laminae defects

Cracked feet

Feet crack because there is too much stress put upon the horn tissue. The most common cause I come across is due to an interruption to the force that is travelling up the horn tube to the coronary band. In other words, there is not a straight line between the bottom on the foot and the top. (fig 13) Force will always look for the shortest route. Therefore if there is an interruption to this route, for instance a ridge around the

Fig 13 – Cracked Foot

Here is a foot that will often crack down the wall due to the flare as indicated by (a). This is because when the constant ground pressure travels up the horn it encounters a ledge, and it is at this point that the wall will give way. This often coincides with the nail exit. (e)
The Coronary band on this type of foot is often at an angle (b) which in turn leads to the opposite wall from the crack being more upright and less liable to crack.
The flare must be removed (f) and the opposite side of the foot must have an extension on the shoe (d) in order to balance the coronary band. (c).

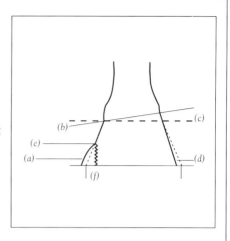

Fig 14 – Dorsal Crack

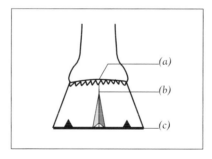

This figure shows a front view of a cracked foot. If the crack is in the position shown, (the toe) then you will usually find a depression in the coronary band at the top to the crack (a). This may be due to the hoof having taken a bad knock in this area, or perhaps due to strain at the point of production. The crack will sometimes remain as a narrow line until it reaches some way down the foot, and then it may open out to be much wider. (b) This can be due to the laminae coming under more strain as the crack grows down the foot. It is often possible to alleviate the strain by filing the toe back in order to make it more upright. If this cannot be achieved without going inside the pastern/ hoof axis, then x-rays would have to be used.This is the method I would favour before mechanically trying to join the two parts together with staples etc., however, I would always shoe this foot with a medial and lateral clip to give the foot more stability. (c) In severe cases I 'frog load' the foot with a short tongued heart bar shoe.

Fig 15 – Quarter Crack

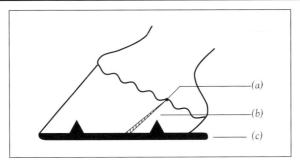

— (a)

— (b)

— (c)

This figure shows a crack running down the foot at an angle from the coronary band to the ground. These cracks are usually on the outside of the foot and are more common in the hind feet. The crack in this foot is caused by pressure in the heel area, and the section behind the crack (b) can often be under so much strain that it breaks away and moves independently from the rest of the hoof wall. The depression found at the top of the crack can frequently create a valley in the foot along the length of the crack as it grows down. (a) I find the most effective treatment is to alleviate some of the weight from the coronary band in this area by fitting a bar shoe to offer rigidity, and applying frog pressure to relieve concussion from the coronary band. I also make a clip in the shoe to sit either side of the crack to help prevent movement, and make sure the shoes are fitted long enough to support the heels (c).

foot where the nail protrudes from the horn, then usually cracks will appear.

To avoid having cracked feet, make sure that the feet are meeting the ground with a level presentation. Then remove any defects from the surface of the horn, without going inside the hoof/pastern axis. It is important to ensure that the angle of the foot is the same on the inside (medial) as on the outside (lateral).

If this is not the case then you must either: Take off the flare, if one exists, or attach a shoe with an extension, even if this involves shoeing wide on the inside. (This can be bevelled off to avoid the shoe being stepped on.) By maintaining the hoof/pastern axis at an acceptable angle, you will notice that the feet will improve due to the force of the concussion being able to travel from the ground surface to the coronary band at an evenly distributed rate all around the foot.

Some cracks will be due to the pastern/hoof axis being incorrect. The stress upon the horn producing area sends out splits in the horn which can vary in size. A very common crack is in the lateral and medial quarter of the foot, often found in overweight youngsters. If these cracks are present then I find that it is necessary to weight load the frog to relieve the pressure on the horn, this will also serve the purpose of helping a better blood supply to the foot, which is an essential part of eliminating the cracks altogether in the long term.

If after this treatment there is still no change, then, and only then, would I look at the possible defects within the animal itself, and talk over with the Vet what possible action needs to be taken in order to improve the quality of horn. I have to say that this is hardly ever necessary.

Flat feet. (Fig 16)

It is very seldom that a foal is born with what we have come to call *flat feet*. That is with a dropped sole, collapsed heels, enlarged frog, and in some cases evidence of a prolapsed digital cushion. Most foals are born with good feet, although they may take some time to reach the correct position. So what happens? Well I believe in some cases the problem starts with the Vet and Farrier not being called in to see the horse early in its development. Too may times I have been presented with a yearling that has foot problems, only to learn that I am the first professional to have seen it since its birth.

This is a result of a breakdown in communications between the team and the owner. We (the professionals) must make sure that the owner

Fig 16 – Flat Foot

This is what we call a flat foot. This is because P3 is almost parallel with the ground surface, thus producing a flat sole (b). The dorsal wall (a) is parallel to P3 which is correct, but because the heels (e) have collapsed, the angle of the dorsal wall to the ground is not upright enough.
Graduated heel shoes would not help this foot. (See fig 28). The bulbs of the heels (d) have prolapsed and are almost touching the ground. The deep flexor tendon (c) is under strain, so too is the pastern joint (f).

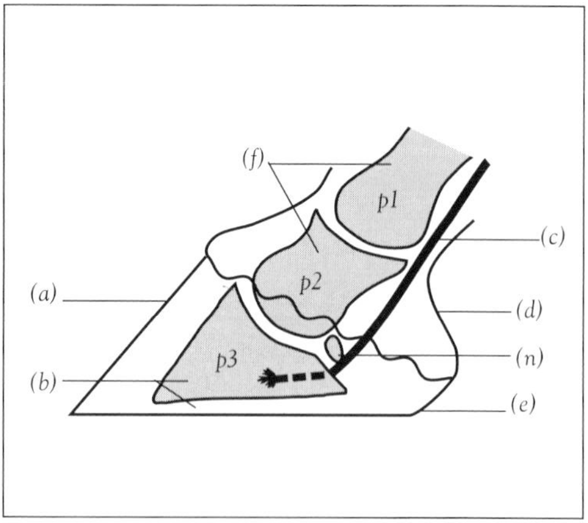

presents the animal to us as soon as possible and not be tempted to wait until there is something wrong. Feet left unchecked at an early stage can start to take on the characteristics of a flat footed horse, and a good Farrier will recognize this and make sure that the horse is looked at regularly. Obesity can also be the start of flat feet as in the early years the hoof will collapse under the weight.

Flat feet are quite common in the race horse as the concern for losing a shoe means that the heels of the shoe are often sloped at the same pitch as the heel of the foot, which restricts the support to the caudal (rear) third of the foot. Although over a short period of time this may not cause too much damage, in the long term the lack of support can lead to the pedal bone rotating into a position that will create a flat foot. I have also come across a close cousin of this type of shoeing in the hunting field and until the upright heel came back into fashion, there were more and more hunters being admitted to the Clinic with this problem.

I believe that flat feet are man-made and therefore man can, and must, stop the problem before it starts. If the pedal bone is flat within the foot capsule then we must support the caudal third and weight load the frog behind the deep flexor attachment. If this is carried out in time it will assist in the re-alignment of the laminae at the point of production.

Corns (fig 17)

Corns are caused by pressure and are more common in the shod horse. They can be so bad as to incapacitate a horse. They are not as common as they used to be because the short-shod, sloped heeled horse is not in such evidence these days.

However, the area where corns occur is one of the most important areas when it comes to support of the horse, and if the shoe is either short or tight fitting, then the chance of corns occurring is greatly increased. If deep-seated corns are present but no visible signs are in evidence on the surface, not only is it possible for the horse to be sound, but when a support shoe is fitted the animal could actually go lame! This is because while the corn area is being concussed, the laminae can be, for want of a better word, calloused, and it is not until the pressure is relieved that the bruised area starts to deteriorate, resulting in a septic corn.

With this in mind, I give support by shoeing long making sure that pressure on the heel is eased gradually to allow the re-absorption of the

Fig 17 – Corns

This figure indicates where you should look for a corn. These are very common if the shoes are too short or have been left on for too long. You will often notice on this type of foot that the frog is enlarged.

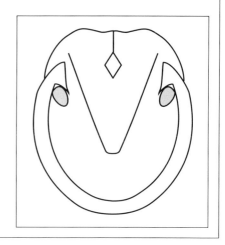

damaged tissue internally. If I suspect that a horse has a deep-seated corn, I always make sure the Vet agrees with my diagnosis.

I have heard Farriers say that the reason some of their horses get corns is because the owner has left the shoes on too long! This, I believe, is the fault of the Farrier who should take on the responsibility of regular shoeing appointments for all of his clients. When I shoe a horse, I always insist that it is booked in for its next appointment before it leaves, and if the owner does not comply, then my professionalism is being questioned and I see no point in continuing the relationship.

Laminae defects

Although you could claim that almost every foot fault is due to or can cause laminae defects, I will use this section to talk about leverage to the laminae. This could be due to unattended feet.

I do not consider that a horse in a field is in a 'natural environment', therefore the feet do not look after themselves as they might in a dry, sandy environment, which is far more indigenous to its ancestry.

If laminae are allowed to grow out of balance, then it follows that leverage will occur. It can manifest itself in many ways, one of which is long toes. (fig 18) These can look quite unassuming but underneath the horn the laminae can be tearing themselves away from the inner structures of the foot, much like prising the skin away from under a finger nail, and this can lead to white lines disease, (seedy toe), collapsed

The Horse's Foot and Related Problems

Fig 18 – Long Toe

A case of long toe and slight heel growth.
This can be corrected in one trimming without effecting the animal in an adverse way.
The full advantages of correcting this foot will be more noticeable to the owner when riding down hill than at any other time, because the horse is now able to break the foot over earlier and so extension becomes much easier.
Line (a) must be straight from the top to the bottom of the foot.
Line (b) is the ground level of the foot after trimming.

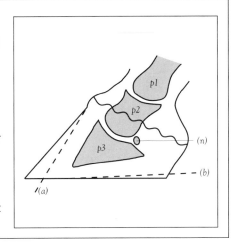

Fig 19 – Long Toe and Heel

Long toe and heel.
This foot has lost the ability to have an effective frog.
When this type of foot is viewed with the foot on the ground there appears to be little wrong with it, however, as the last point of support (a) moves further and further forward, the possibility of the heels collapsing is greatly increased.

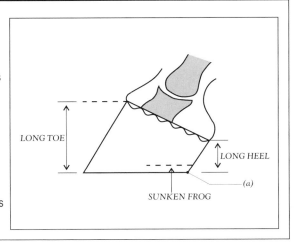

heels, laminitis and may other related problems. Feet that have grown evenly in length can be deceptive and in fact look alright, (fig 19) but they too can hide a multitude of problems, most notable being the fact that the frog is no longer able to do its job properly, and this can lead to circulation difficulties and in some cases even infection. Some types of horses are actively encouraged to have feet like this in order to create a false action, for instance the Tennessee Walkers. I feel that it stretches

Fig 20 – White Lines Disease

This figure shows the separation in the white line and the break down of the attachment of the sole to the wall. (a)
The most effective way to deal with this is to expose the bacteria to the air as this will kill them off and prevent the wall parting from the laminae.
Be careful not to create a hole when clearing away the black rubbish in the infected area as you will never be able to thoroughly remove ALL the bacteria, and the problem will just start off all over again.

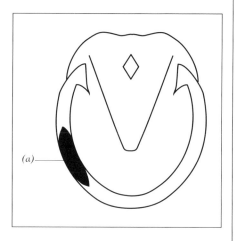

Fig 21 – White Lines Disease

This figure shows the white lines disease resected and removed from the area. (a)
After this procedure there is little chance of the disease returning. The area should be kept clean and dry.It is far better to take preventative action to stop this disease taking hold in the first place and this can be easily done by ensuring that you clean out any impurities in the white line every time you shoe a horse.
I always recommend a supportive shoe with clips to offer more stability and rigidity to the foot. (b)

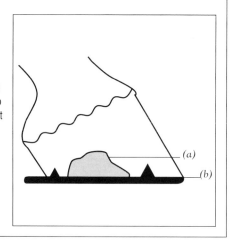

our ethics somewhat to fit shoes that we know could possibly cause such defects just to achieve a particular action purely for aesthetics.

Laminae defects should be identified as early as possible. In the case of white line disease it will first show itself as a blackening of the white line. This should be removed and cleaned out regularly to kill off the bacteria. In chronic cases it is better to resect the effected area and leave

Fig 22 – Shoe Fitting

This shows the front view of a foot, cut away to demonstrate the fitting of a shoe that is seated out. (b) The centre line (c) runs through the frog, (a) and through BP2 and on to BP1.

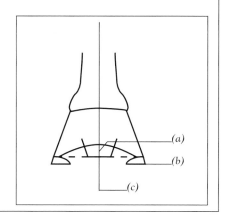

it exposed to the air. This will kill off the bacteria as they are anaerobic, but only do this with the permission of the Vet. (figs 20 & 21)

In very bad cases of laminae defect I would always request an x-ray in order to see what is going on inside the foot and to get an idea of how much horn there is to work with.

While shoeing some of the horses that have been referred to the Clinic, I have noticed what looks like bruising around the toe of the foot when the shoe has been removed. This, in the past, has usually been put down to concussion due to road work etc., however, I have found this not always to be the case. If the colour change in the toe has a yellow surround, then there is a good chance that the laminae are being levered away or towards the pedal bone. When this is corrected, the so-called bruising does not return. Laminitis is dealt with in another section.

Types of shoes:

Surgical shoes in inexperienced hands are very dangerous. If incorrectly fitted they can lead to horses being given short or long term lameness and, at worst, being put down!

Most Farriers these days use ready-made shoes, the standard of which is improving all the time. I have to say at this point that the worst shoe I have ever seen was one that was hand made. Personally I only use wide section shoes, and would not put on anything thicker than 10mm or 3/8 of an inch. (This does not include shires). I believe that by using these shoes I can achieve better action, and that concession problems are less. The shoes have to be seated out well to avoid sole pressure,

---

Fig 23 – The Heart Bar shoe

This shoe is particularly good for laminitics who are in need of frog support.
The centre tongue (a) can be made much shorter to produce a shoe that is appropriate for a horse with collapsed heels.
The dotted line indicates the position of the heels and the frog beneath the shoe.

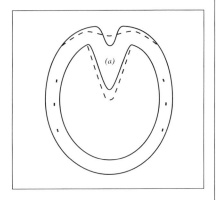

Fig 24 – Fitting a Heart Bar shoe

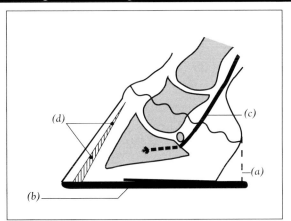

This is a surgical shoe for laminitis, but if fitted incorrectly can cause severe damage to the animal.
I strongly recommend that when fitting these shoes there is a Vet present and that you have lateral x-rays of all the feet that need a heart bar shoe fitted.
If pressure is going to be applied to the frog then it must extend in front (towards the toe) of the attachment of the deep flexor tendon (b), but not too far forward as to crush the blood supply within the terminal arch. The pressure must be enough to counter-act the forces being placed upon it by the deep flexor tendon (c), and the unstable attachment of the laminae at the coronary band (d).The foot should be shod long in order to give support at the heel. This will enable the horse to take some of its weight off the hind feet (a).
DO NOT fit a heart bar shoe if you are unsure of the consequences.

therefore there is a little more work involved. I will not put on a sloped heel hunter shoe as I am fully aware of the damage that sloped heels and tight foot shoeing can induce. I believe that heels should be upright and fully supportive to the animal. (figs 12 & 22)

Heart-bar (figs 23 & 24)

This I find a very useful shoe because with the back-up of x-rays it is possible to weight load the frog for a period of time in order to relieve pressure on another part of the foot. In the case of laminitis it really proves its worth as it not only relieves most of the pain but it also acts as a long term cure.

This shoe can also be used to help sand cracks, collapsed heels, white lines disease and many other foot defects. I often use what I call a short tongue heart-bar just to give a horse extra support, even if there is no obvious defect present.

With all caudal third problems the relationship between the tongue of the shoe, and the deep flexor tendon attachment to the pedal bone, is a very important one. I would always inform the Vet of what I would like to do in order to avoid any mis-understanding, and in most cases would work with radiographs.

Egg-bar (figs 25 & 26)

This is also a shoe that I like to use quite often but I find that you have

Fig 25 – Fitting an egg bar shoe

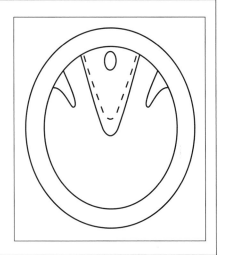

This figure shows the ground surface of the foot with an egg bar shoe fitted to it.
Note how the back of the shoe covers the bulbs of the heels.
The dotted line indicates where frog support should be placed if it is added to the shoe.
This is a very good shoe for giving caudal support for a horse at rest.

to be careful with regard to how long you use it without frog support. The danger is that the central bone column within the foot is not being supported and this can result in causing more trouble than you are curing.

It is without doubt a good shoe for tendon, ligament, and collapsed heel problems, but I do tend to use it with frog support.

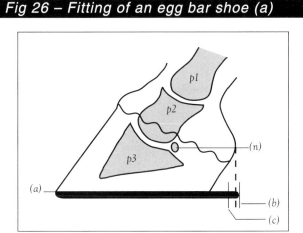

Fig 26 – Fitting of an egg bar shoe (a)

An egg bar shoe can be fitted too long and this will lead to the horse putting its foot down heel first. I always fit an egg bar to a line 1/8 of an inch longer than a line taken straight down from the bulb of the heel. (b)
The only exception I make is when the horse is in work, when I tend to bring the shoe to 1/8 of an inch within the line (c). Bear in mind that I would usually attach the longer shoe when a horse has a tendon problem and is at rest.
I strongly recommend that if this type of shoe is to be used for a long period, then frog support is needed.

Straight bar (fig 27)

This shoe is a good 'between' shoe. It has some of the support of the heart bar and some of the length of the egg bar. I find it very useful for competition horses in need of support because it is easier to keep out of harm's way.

With an extended frog tongue, this shoe can be used in the early stages of collapsed heels, false quarter, sand cracks and weak heels. You will find, that if fitted correctly, the feet will improve.

Fig 27 – Fitting a straight bar shoe

In this figure you can just see the bulbs of the heels protruding from the back of the shoe.

The frog tongue (a) is in the centre of the bar across the shoe and can assist in giving frog pressure.

This is a useful shoe for giving the foot rigidity and caudal support.

If the tongue is made longer, then this shoe is good for horses in work who have pre-navicular syndrome.

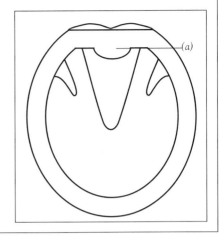

Fig 28 – Graduated Heel Shoe

This is to show the effect of attaching a graduated heel shoe simply to improve the dorsal wall angle as a result of the heels having been crushed.

Each time I see one of these shoes being used under these conditions I have noticed that the pastern and caudal (rear) third of the foot have been under stress. (c)

(a)   Graduated heel shoe.

(b)   Heels crushed and unable to take the weight.

Please refer to the section entitled, *Laminitis for the Vet and Farrier* for the only time I use this type of shoe.

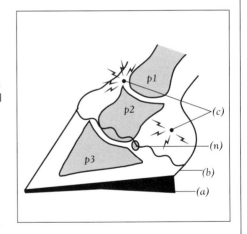

Graduated or wedged heel (fig 28)

This shoe is often used for aesthetic reasons only.

It is very tempting to think that by propping up the heel you can re-align the inner structures of the foot. The problem lies in the misunderstood concept that by raising the heel of the shoe you are in fact raising the heel of the foot.

Fig 29 – A lateral view of a plastic heart bar shoe

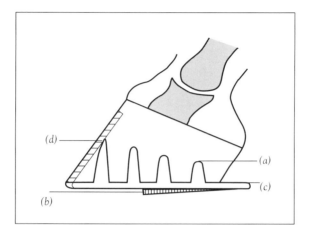

(a) = Plastic tabs that stick the shoe to the wall of the foot. The wall should be prepared by sanding and cleaning with an anti-grease agent. When fitting there should be no air trapped behind the tab, and sticking should be done as quickly as possible. When replacing the tabs it pays to use an electric sander or file to remove the old glue as they must be absolutely smooth before re-sticking.

(b) = An extra plastic tapered wedge that I stick on to the centre tongue when shoeing for a laminitic with a retracted frog. This can be altered as the frog recovers.

(c) = The shoe must have good heel length in order to support the classic laminitic stance of fore feet placed well forward.

(d) = This shows the area (not actual size) that would be resected if a dorsal resection had been performed. Note that the break-over point of the foot is moved back since if it is left too far out it will place pressure on the laminae at the point of production.

Instead you are directing the point of concussion on the heel closer to the ground. The resulting concussion is absorbed in the caudal part of the foot and at the pastern, which is now being forced into a different angle.

The only time I would use this shoe is when I come across a long heeled foot which I need to lower to its correct level gradually over a period of two to five weeks, in order to avoid undue strain being put upon the tendons and muscles.

Plastic shoes (fig 29)

The type of plastic shoe that I use is a stick-on, and I use these shoes a great deal, particularly for laminitics since I do not like to nail a shoe on to a horse that may be in pain. They are easy to adjust whilst still on the foot. In some cases I find that stick-on aluminium shoes are also worth using.

Light weight
Light weight shoes i.e. aluminium, are very useful for horses who have trouble keeping shoes on. Smaller nails can be used and there is less resistance to the nails, although road work must be kept to a minimum.

The Horse's Foot and Related Problems

— 5 —
Laminitis – for the owner

When a horse gets laminitis, the owner's first reaction is to blame themselves, but it is not necessarily their fault. The first thing to do is to make sure that your Team is aware of the situation. Once this is established, then you can start to isolate how the laminitis came about.

Why has my horse got laminitis?
Four complaints very common in the laminitic:-
1) A long- or short-term build up of toxins within the gut, due to unbalanced feeding.
2) Sudden stress on the animal. i.e. colic etc.,
3) Placenta retention.
4) Direct concussion on the laminae through road work etc.

Diet imbalance:
In cases that are related to diet, we have first to understand how the digestive system of the horse works. A horse has a very small stomach and its whole system is designed to run mainly on fibre, and if an owner understands that, then the chances of their horse getting this type of laminitis is very greatly reduced.

In chapter 12 on Diet, Fig 37 shows a simplified version of the horses' gut. If too many soluble sugars reach the rear gut without first being properly digested in the stomach and small intestine, the subsequent build up of toxins make their way into the blood through the gut wall.

This, in turn, causes blood pressure to build up, triggering a by-pass system in certain areas, one being the laminae. This we call toxic shock.

If your horse is either a gelding or a mare that is not in foal, you must be aware that you do not own, what nature would term, a 'normal' horse. The 'normal' or 'natural' horse makes use of the good grass that is produced in spring, summer and sometimes autumn, because it is then that a stallion needs quick response energy to either cover mares or fight off competition, and a mare to lactate or carry a foal.

Once you take away these natural functions you must be mindful of the problems that may emerge, especially if the horse is not working. If the horse is not working then it will only need enough food to keep in good condition, not to build up muscle or fat.

I must mention again at this point that there are professionals who know how to create a balanced diet for your animal, and I advise all Vets to make a dietician part of the Team. By doing this you will find that the horse will be more consistent and internally balanced for its work load.

The majority of horses are fed by amateurs.

Stress:

Horses can suffer stress for many and various reasons. A sudden change in diet or environment; excitement in anticipation of a hunt or show; anxiety of separation; weaning; fear of travelling etc,. How you horse copes with this stress can be influenced by whether he is on a balanced and consistent diet, for if the gut does start to spasm when it contains mostly fibre, there is less likelihood of excess soluble energy being forced into the rear gut, where the digestive process is least able to cope with it.

It seems that some horses react differently to the same situation. For example when boxing to the show one may become genuinely agitated and stressed resulting in colic or other gut related problems, whereas another may just become slightly distressed or excited. Both show up initially as loose and frequent droppings, as the food in the gut gets forced through the system quicker than it should.

Placenta retention:

Placenta retention is another possible cause of laminitis. It occurs when the mare, after foaling retains a piece of the placenta and the very high protein content is re-absorbed into the blood supply, once again causing an imbalance.

Concussion:

Direct concussion to the laminae can be caused in many ways. Road work is one example. It is not natural for a horse to have that level of concussion to the attachment system within the hoof capsule. It follows that if this attachment system (the laminae) is subjected to too much concussion, the horse will get laminitis, albeit of a type that is not brought about through the usual channels.

Stress to the blood supply solely within the foot is a very common cause of laminitis. This can be caused by leverage of the wall laminae away from the bone laminae, either due to the toe being too long or one side of the foot being longer than the other.

Despite already having the above knowledge, some are still willing to take the chance of their horse or pony getting the disease. I am thinking of the showing fraternity in particular, who, it seems, have to present an animal on the verge of laminitis, in order to achieve a place in the prize money.

What to do:

If your animal does go down with laminitis then you, as the owner, must be sure that you can offer the best conditions to treat the animal, particularly if it has to be stabled for a long period. The horse must not become bored, too thin, too fat, stressed or out of condition. It is going to be taken out of its normal environment, away from sunlight, earth, grass and perhaps even company, yet it is important not to place it under any more stress than is absolutely necessary. Your Vet or dietician will advise you on vitamins and minerals to supplement the loss of sunlight, earth and grass, and only you will be able to judge whether the horse is happy or not on its own. Ensure that all work around the animal is done quietly and calmly. At the Clinic we feed all our horses at ground level as this is the natural feeding position of a horse.

If for some reason you find yourself without immediate access to professional advice then bring the horse in, give it fresh water (spring water if possible) and **high fibre, low energy hay.** (It is then imperative that you contact a Vet.)

I would advise any of the following types of hay

1) Hay, that despite containing grasses like rye, clover etc., (normally not recommended for laminitics) has been cut late in the season and is a FIRST CUT, so that its energy level is not very high.

2) Hay that is made from grasses that are low in energy so that even if they are cut at the height of the season (May-June) they would not cause a problem to the laminitic.

3) Threshed hay. This is hay that is discarded by the seed industry after their harvest. It is very low in energy but high in fibre.

If in doubt, mix some good oat straw with your hay in order to make it less palatable to the animal and thus spread the feeding time over a longer period. Remember that a horse's digestive system is designed to cope with the animal eating 18 out of every 24 hours, so in the case of a laminitic this can be achieved by making sure that the hay intake is of low energy and high fibre so that it can, and must be fed ad lib. You can ask your Vet to have your hay tested to ascertain its energy content etc. We test owner's hay regularly at the Clinic and often find it alone has been enough to give the animal laminitis.

The way in which we assess hay samples is to show the different grass types present and their feed values, along with recommendations for the uses of that particular hay. Our standard analysis form is reproduced opposite.

Other food can be given to the horse provided it just maintains good condition without heating up the animal. At the Clinic I feed a very carefully weighed diet of sugar-beet, bran or crushed oats, limestone flour, kelp, cod-liver oil, molasses and ad-lib organic, late cut, hay and spring water. We find this to be a very passive diet and even youngsters that are admitted seem to thrive without becoming overheated.

Bedding for a laminitic should be supportive to the feet without being too deep. It is important that the horse is not standing on an unlevel surface as this will put stress on one area more than another, so if the horse is not wanting to lie down a lot, do not use much bedding. At the Clinic we bed down on rubber thermo mats. These are ideal as they present a level and shock absorbing surface. Onto these, in a small area of the stable, we put down some shavings for soiling and staining. If you are only using shavings remember that they dry out the feet and make them very hard. This does not help the healing process as the foot, or feet, are needing to expand and contract all the time, so do not use too many shavings and damp them down a little with a disinfectant solution. When using straw I find that it is more difficult to maintain a level surface for the feet, and to ensure that the feet bear the weight of the animal evenly without any 'balling up', which could cause pressure on the sole.

At Greatcombe Clinic we also provide a box covered with 6" of peat which we thoroughly soak, then allow the horse or pony to stand in it for up to four hours at a time. This is a useful way of making the feet supple and yet at the same time giving them support.

To sum up

Whatever the cause of laminitis, the foot will not always be hot, and the animal will not always be lame. It can effect one or all four feet. The animal may be just a little stiff, or just not themselves, or have recently suffered some stress, a bout of colic for example. However, once the imbalance has reached the foot or feet, it resembles a blood blister under your finger nail.

GREATCOMBE CLINIC HAY ANALYSIS REPORT

Customer   Date

GENERAL REMARKS

COLOUR
SMELL
TEXTURE
SEED STATE

GRASS TYPES

HIGH FEED VALUE		LOW FEED VALUE	
Italian Rye Grass		Crested Dog's Tail	
Perennial Rye Grass		Sweet Vernal	
Timothy		Agrostis (Bent Grass)	
Meadow Fescue		Yorkshire Fog	
Cocksfoot		Buttercup	
Smooth Meadow Grass		Plantain	
Clover		Dock	

E.D.V.	SCALE FIG:

RECOMMENDED FEEDING SUGGESTIONS

- AT REST Up to 2 hours work per week
- LIGHT WORK Hacking up to 1 hour per day
- HEAVY WORK Hunting, Eventing, Point-to-Point
- IN FOAL Last 3 months gestation
- LAMINITIC

In severe cases (chronic) the pressure has to be relieved (resection) {fig 33} and support given. See Chapter 6 for more information. In mild cases (acute) having the feet well balanced and trimmed regularly may often be enough. I would always recommend having the feet x-rayed at the first opportunity in order to see how much damage may have been done to the internal structures, and later to use as a reference by the Vet and Farrier.

If laminitis is diagnosed early enough and the right treatment given, then the prognosis is always much more favourable. A *good team* will be very aware of this.

— 6 —
Laminitis – for Vet & Farrier

Laminitis, once diagnosed, is in some part always going to be a mechanical lameness. If the Farrier and Vet don't get together and apply treatment immediately, then the result is usually disaster.

First let's talk, (in simple terms), about what has happened within the foot capsule.

The reaction that has taken place in the foot is between the bone (P3) and the attachment of the horn, and can be compared in human terms, with a blood blister forming under the nail. In the mildest cases the horn swells at the point of production, a small ridge is formed which then grows out at the bottom of the foot. These cases are much more common than people may like to believe. Many horses that are enduring excessive road work go through this procedure quite frequently.

X-rays must be taken as soon as is physically possible. (See Radiology section)

If the case of laminitis is worse, then there is more serious activity within the foot capsule. This may involve the wall being diverted away from the hoof/pastern axis, or the bone (P3) being rotated towards the ground (figs 30 & 31), or both. These movements happen because of an interruption to the blood supply of the laminae. In even worse cases the bone structure migrates south en masse and is classed a 'sinker'. (fig 32)

In a mild case the frog can be given support to just in front of the deep flexor tendon attachment by a heart bar shoe with heel length, and the foot dressed parallel to p3. You will find that in these cases the horse will hardly go lame and can be back in work relatively quickly.

In the case where the wall has been pushed out from the correct hoof/pastern axis but the bone has not rotated, (capsule rotation) (fig 30) then you must return the foot to its original angle. This should be done with the aid of x-rays. Heel growth is often great in these cases, however, beware of over trimming as this will effect the deep flexor tendon. If the heel is very long take it down to its correct position, and then put on a wedge heel shoe with frog support, gradually lowering it over a period of time. The angle of the dorsal wall will vary from breed

Fig 30 – Rotation

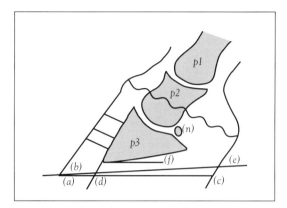

A foot showing rotation of P3. .... or is it?

P3 is out of line with p2 and p1. You can also see that the distance between p3 and the wall becomes thicker towards the ground surface. This does not necessarily mean that P3 is rotated.

You can do some simple calibrations on the x-ray plate to help in diagnosing a laminitic.

(a) Angle of dorsal wall before trimming.

(b) Angle of dorsal wall after heels have been trimmed.

(c) Amount of heel to be removed.

(d) Angle of p3 in relation to dorsal wall.

(e) Ground level after trimming.

(f) Angle of p3 compared to the ground.

Before starting work on these feet we must realise that there is movement in the pedal joint all the time. That means that if you alter the heel length of a foot, then the pedal joint will always move a certain amount to compensate.

After removing the heel length (c) the toe angle that was 55% becomes 49%.

To return this to 55% you may come across damaged horny laminae tissue. This must be removed in order to balance the foot, but this amount of trimming is better done with a Vet present. This foot should be supported with a heart bar shoe, and regularly balanced.

to breed, and I find that the thoroughbred can range from 50 to 56 degrees in front and between 2-5 degrees more, in hinds. The cob type will usually have an angle that is up to 3 degrees steeper than the thoroughbred. Either breed usually performs better in the middle of its range.

If P3 has rotated then you must give support to the area just forward of the deep flexor tendon, and in most cases resect. (fig 33) Heart bar shoes must only be put on with the aid of x-rays, and in the case of laminitis, a Vet should be present. First the foot, or feet, must be x-rayed with the relevant markers in place on the foot. See Radiology chapter. These are reference points for the Farrier, as he/she must be sure where the centre tongue of the shoe has to be placed in relation to the attachment of the deep flexor tendon, and the blood supply to the foot.

As more frog support is required in bad cases, you must relieve the pressure built up by serum in the laminae. It may not be present in every case but the dorsal wall needs to be weakened in order to relieve the pressure being put upon the laminae by the re-rotation of P3.

It is sometimes possible to leave the laminae membrane between the dermal and epidermal laminae, and this helps avoid secondary infection. The resection should be kept clean with a disinfectant but also allowed to dry.

The shoe MUST be seated out so that no pressure is being applied to the sole, since this can be disastrous to the vascular process. Extra heel length in the shoe is also important to the comfort of the animal since it will still want to present all four feet in a forward position.

Heart bar shoes can be used for a long time providing the frog stays healthy. In my experience once the wall has grown down about 1/3 of the overall foot length, it is possible to rest the frog for a period of about 7-10 days on clean, dry bedding. (Wood shavings being the most suitable).

I would always recommend putting on a very thin shoe with heel length to support the animal while the frog is being rested.

If the frog tongue is fitted correctly, the frog should be able to produce healthy tissue even with the extra pressure upon it, however this should be carefully monitored each time the shoes are removed.

All shoes should be as thin as possible to enable the foot to work at its maximum efficiency.

Due to the lack of healthy wall at the toe, it is very easy to allow the medial and lateral quarters of the foot to grow out. Not only does this create flared quarters, but also, due to the separation of the laminae at the toe, any leverage on that part of the wall will encourage white lines disease, making it more difficult to achieve a good attachment for the shoe, and to maintain a good foot shape later on.

As the foot starts to grow down it is important to ensure that you keep the correct hoof/pastern axis because the wall will have a tendency to grow out of alignment.

If the sole is soft, do not remove it as this will cause the sensitive sole to prolapse very quickly. The best way of relieving fluid pressure on the

Fig 31 – Rotation

This figure shows a laminitic with rotation of the pedal bone (P3).
The angle of the wall at the toe (a) is correct but the bone has rotated from its true angle (b)and this creates a wedge of damaged laminae (c).
The sole on this foot has dropped and will also have internal damage.

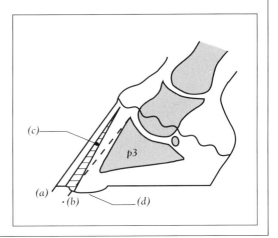

Fig 32 – Sinker

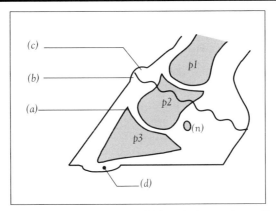

If the separation of the laminae is too severe (b) then the bone column will sink, creating the sinker. After P3 has sunk (a) you will be able to feel a depression above the coronary band all the way around the foot. (c) As with other laminitics the sole will often be proud of the ground surface. (d) These laminitic cases are the worst and most severe, and are much harder to treat effectively. It is really only possible if you catch the disease early enough and have a very good team on the job. The horse has to be regularly monitored and the shoes altered frequently.

The shoe I use on a sinker is an adjustable heart bar. I find the plastic stick-on shoe far kinder for this job and much easier to alter once attached.

As a Farrier I would not attempt to touch a sinker without an equine Vet being present. Prognosis poor.

Fig 33 – Dorsal Wall Resection

This figure shows the resected toe of a laminitic.

In order to be effective the resection should be wide enough and high enough to allow for the re-rotation of p3 and the removal of the laminitic wedge.

The epidermal laminae are exposed (a) and they should be kept clean and allowed to dry. The wall (b) that is at the boundary of the resection should be clean and have a definite edge.

The animal should feel no pain when this is performed and a heart bar shoe (I prefer to use a plastic shoe) should be attached as soon as the resection is completed.

In this figure you can see the plastic tabs that keep the shoe attached. (c)

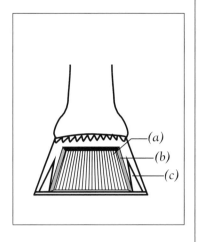

sole is to go in through the toe, but once again this can only be carried out in the presence of a Vet.

Any drugs should only be given in the knowledge that P3 is being correctly supported by heart bar shoes.

Explaining Laminitis and it prevention by Robert Eustace, is one of the most comprehensive books on the subject.

YOUR NOTES

7

Navicular & Caudal Third Lameness

Over the years navicular disease has become easier to identify mainly due to the fact that the interpretation of radiographs has become more of a science. It is becoming clear that in the past some types of lameness which have been attributed to navicular, were in fact due to imbalances within the hoof capsule. It is these diagnoses that have high-lighted the caudal third lameness as a separate problem from navicular, although the former can lead to the latter.

If the lameness has been identified as navicular, and treatment is recommended, then it is another example of when the Farrier and Vet should co-operate to ensure that the treatment is working effectively. It should be recognised that if the lameness is due to a circulation problem, then its cause must be correctly identified as such, for instance was the foot being constricted, and if so, where, and by how much. Treatment will not be so effective if the foot, or feet, are not properly balanced. The vascular process is at its most inefficient when the feet are unbalanced and although the recommended drug treatment is mainly concerned with the dilation of the blood supply, even this can only be achieved if the whole system is in full working order.

The egg bar shoe, with accurate frog support, is most effective in observing whether the blood supply will respond to treatment, because it will give caudal third support and can be frog loaded (figs 25 & 27) to alleviate pressure from the heels. Response to this shoe is relatively quick since the horse finds it easier to rest the back of the foot, even in movement.

The horse with very long heels, despite a good dorsal wall angle, (fig 19) (another prime candidate for caudal third lameness) needs to regain frog pressure. This can not always be accomplished immediately as the re-alignment of the inner structures are better achieved if allowed to change slowly. Frog support will be necessary.

In all cases of caudal third lameness or navicular it is only possible to fit an accurate shoe with the benefit of radiographs. From these we are able to observe the position of P3 in the hoof capsule which will in turn be an indication of damage being inflicted to the caudal third. The more flat the presentation the more strain will be placed on the deep flexor tendon. This strain may be absorbed in the foot, the pastern, the fetlock, the knee, the shoulder or even the back, so that the horse may not always be lame while the changes are taking place, but the animal will often be more susceptible to bruises or strains.

Fig 16 shows the most common foot with CAUDAL THIRD problems.

Is it possible for a horse to inherit caudal third lameness as a result of its bloodline? I believe it is... let me explain.

If a foal inherits a long pastern conformation from its sire or dam, and then is either allowed to become too fat or is shod without support, or both, it is more likely to put stress on the caudal third of the foot than a horse with the correct hoof/pastern axis.

It is crucial that the Farrier and Vet understand how the caudal third of the foot responds to different work loads, different types of shoeing and treatment. This is where I find dissection so useful. A good exercise is to dissect a foot from the heel to the toe at the angle of the horn production. When I first did this I was quite surprised at the amount of soft tissue that had to be cut away before reaching the wings of P3. This soft tissue will not only back up the natural conformation of the animal but will also go on to take part in any alteration that may occur due to work load. If you observe the weight load taken on the fore-leg fetlock at the gallop, you will notice that the pastern will often be parallel to the ground, and although this is normal, it has to be supported. Likewise in the hind leg when landing from a jump, or even if carrying too much weight, particularly if it has long pasterns. In this situation you will find that the horse wants to put the hind foot down further forward in order to alleviate the weight from the fore limb and in the long term this may result in the heels being unable to take the extra strain and, if left unsupported, would cause the heels to prolapse.

We buy horses for all sorts of reasons and whims. Sometimes it can be that we simply like the colour, but more often than not it is the conformation of the animal that helps us to decide whether it is a sensible purchase. When buying a horse the condition of the heels and caudal third of the foot is as important a factor as the condition of its coat, its legs, knees, neck carriage, back movement, jumping ability etc. This important factor should not be overlooked but often a horse with prolapsed heels is passed by the Vet and is proclaimed sound in wind and limb. This goes to prove the necessity of the TEAM as mentioned in Chapter 1. It is essential that both the Vet and the Farrier attend a

Fig 16 – Flat Foot

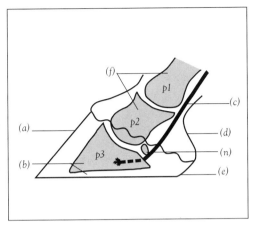

This is what we call a flat foot. This is because P3 is almost parallel with the ground surface, thus producing a flat sole (b). The dorsal wall (a) is parallel to P3 which is correct, but because the heels (e) have collapsed, the angle of the dorsal wall to the ground is not upright enough. Graduated heel shoes would not help this foot. (See fig 28). The bulbs of the heels (d) have prolapsed and are almost touching the ground. The deep flexor tendon (c) is under strain, so too is the pastern joint (f).

Fig 19 – Long Toe and Heel

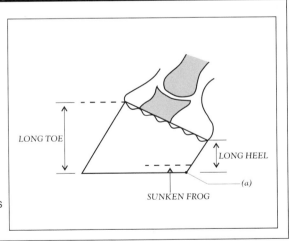

Long toe and heel. This foot has lost the ability to have an effective frog. When this type of foot is viewed with the foot on the ground there appears to be little wrong with it, however, as the last point of support (a) moves further and further forward, the possibility of the heels collapsing is greatly increased.

vetting in order to relieve the Vet from some of the responsibility of passing judgement on the feet. A Farrier will then be able to confer with the Vet and voice concerns that he/she would have if asked to take on the shoeing of that horse.

The caudal third of the foot can often receive a good deal of bruising and this in turn means the horse will have recurring 'puss in foot'. The strain that caudal third lameness places upon the laminae inside the foot can often lead to separation and then on to white line disease, and many other problems related to the hoof capsule.

It is not all gloom and doom however, for if the problem is spotted early enough and judged to be redeemable, and with the right team working together, the horse will begin to make a recovery almost immediately.

—— *8* ——

Radiology – X-Ray

I n this section I will not be going into the complex area of explaining the minute and exact workings of an x-ray machine – Adams and others cover that topic much better than I could. Instead, I would like to concentrate on the x-rays needed by Farriers.

The language:

m.A. (milliamperage) -	the amount of rays you are going to use.
kVp (Kilovoltage peak) -	The potential penetration of the rays.
Exposure time -	how long the rays will be used.
FFD (Focal Film Distance) -	The distance between the machine and the plate.
Collimator -	If the machine is fitted with this then you can adjust the primary beam to be in a confined area.
Central Focal Point -	this is the centre of x-ray alignment.

As a Surgical Farrier, I need to know what is going on inside the horse's foot, and although I might be aware of the anatomy, it is impossible to judge exactly what is happening to the inner structures. This is when an x-ray is so valuable. In my opinion it would be a great advantage to have all feet x-rayed before shoeing a horse for the first time in order to ascertain the correct position and condition of the bone structure, and these x-rays would then stay with the horse throughout its life, and would, I believe, prove very useful in any future diagnoses.

When taking an x-ray for use by a Farrier in the treatment of laminitis, for example, it is most important that both the Farrier and Vet or radiographer, are clear of exactly what is needed. For instance I have a particular way of marking the foot before a lateral x-ray for laminitis and caudal third lameness is taken, and this helps me in the correct shoeing of that animal. (fig 34)

Dorsal Marker

1) The dorsal marker does not have to extend right to the bottom of the foot, but should be long enough to reflect the angle of the dorsal

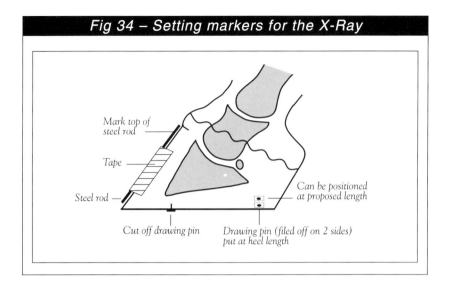

Fig 34 – Setting markers for the X-Ray

Mark top of steel rod

Tape

Steel rod

Cut off drawing pin

Drawing pin (filed off on 2 sides) put at heel length

Can be positioned at proposed length

wall. Mark the foot at the top end of the dorsal marker, so that you can measure the change in future plates taken. Use something substantial as a dorsal marker. I find that if you use thin wire on the dorsal wall it does not always show up clear or straight in the x-ray. If the dorsal wall is not already straight from top to bottom then it must be made so before the x-ray is taken. This can be done with a rasp, being careful to stay on, or outside, the pastern/foot axis.

Even when the foot is weight loaded it is not always correct to assume that the foot will be taking all the forward weight of the animal because the hind feet can, and often do, place themselves forward in order to take weight off the fore feet. There is a lot of natural rotation in the pedal joint, as capsular rotation will show. (fig30) However, that said, when an x-ray for laminitis or caudal third lameness is presented to me, I still need to know whether the foot was weight loaded or not as all information is valuable when trying to make a prognosis.

Frog Marker

2) The frog marker for my x-rays is positioned in the point of the frog. All too often I have been sent x-rays that have the marker in a position that is vaguely described as being 1 cm from the point of the frog. This is most unsatisfactory as it is rather a moveable point depending on the individual who positions it and the state of the frog. I would prefer that the individual responsible for taking the plate has the

frog trimmed at the point and then place a shortened drawing pin in the junction between the frog and the sole. This gives me a fixed reference point from which to measure exactly where to place the support of a heart bar shoe in relation to the attachment of the deep flexor tendon.

Heel marker.

3) I also like a heel marker as this helps me to determine the length of heel that can be trimmed. This is very useful in cases of capsular rotation as I can ascertain whether the P3 is in the correct position but the *wall* is out of balance. This marker should be placed, either at the ground level, or, more preferably, at the point to which the heel will eventually be trimmed. This latter position I find more useful.

4) When taking an x-ray, the foot should be placed on a level block with a wire or lead line attached to the block running parallel to the ground level of the foot (fig 35). This lead line should be placed up against the plate when an x-ray is being taken and should be the central focal point of a lateral x-ray. This marker is particularly helpful in indicating the amount of sole present under P3 at the point of the frog. This information is very useful in cases of capsular rotation because it is then possible to calculate on the x-ray just how much foot needs to be trimmed.

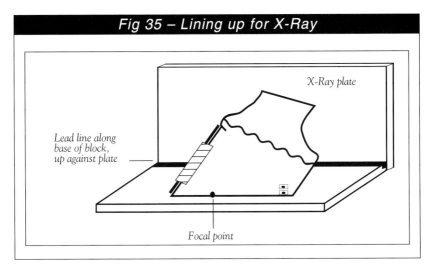

Fig 35 – Lining up for X-Ray

X-Ray plate

Lead line along base of block, up against plate

Focal point

In the cases of caudal third lameness the position of P3 is just as important as in laminitis. It is often the case that the bone will contra rotate, i.e. the bone will be presented too flat within the hoof capsule resulting in FLAT FOOT and all the related problems therein. It is

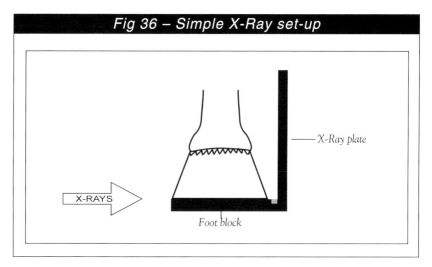

Fig 36 – Simple X-Ray set-up

X-Ray plate

X-RAYS

Foot block

important to know the position of the deep flexor tendon attachment before applying a support shoe.

I find anterior/posterior plates to be more useful in cases of sidebone, massive imbalance of the foot capsule, and in determining asymmetrical problems.

Navicular plates would be used by the Farrier mainly for the same diagnostic reasons as a Vet might use them. The advantage to the Farrier is that he/she is able to note any medial/lateral imbalance which could effect the way the horse is shod.

I find Adams' *Lameness in Horses* a very good reference book for showing the various positions in which a leg should be when taking x-rays.

I strongly recommend that any Farrier that is thinking of doing surgical work should invest in a viewing screen for the purpose of examining x-rays. It is then possible to take time in reaching conclusions, and affords the opportunity to study old x-rays, and thus improve general knowledge in this field. I have found Vets to be most helpful when it comes to obtaining plates from which to learn. Try to locate the defect or, harder still, try to find a foot that has nothing wrong with it!

9

Foot Care

Foot care is one of the big business areas in the equine world today. A lot of people buy quantities of different preparations to help their horses' feet. I suggest that you only use something that has been recommended either by your Farrier or your Vet, as all too often I come across people who are trying out very expensive pots of this or that, only to find that they are making no difference at all.

I do not for one minute want to decry the tireless work that is being carried out researching the various complaints that are to be found in the horse's foot, but at Greatcombe Clinic we have found that unless the feet are balanced and the horse is moving correctly, it is difficult to establish whether one preparation or another is truly effective. Having ascertained this, we have found the real need for preparations, foot pads, additives, etc., is virtually nil. Diet will play a very big part in the make up of the foot, and to this end I would always recommend that the owner calls in the dietician to work out a sensible and appropriate diet before you spend money on foot preparations that you may not need.

The foot has a very good system for controlling moisture and, in the right environment, this works very efficiently. However, when the horse is placed on bedding that is moisture absorbing, (i.e. shavings) then obviously a little help is needed. This can be administered by very slightly wetting the bedding, or standing the horse in water for a short period of time. This is what I would recommend for all horses that are stabled and are developing dry, cracked feet. If you apply oil to the feet the *periople* (the control mechanism) will assume that the feet are wet and will therefore shut down the moisture supply, resulting in the dry cracked feet that your regular application of the oil is trying to overcome. If your Farrier or Vet think that your horse has abnormal feet, then the first thing to do is to establish why.

The real issue is whether we are we are applying preparations to the feet simply in order to make them *look better*, and this is a whole different question. I look forward to the day when it doesn't matter whether you have oil on the feet or not, when it doesn't make the difference of a place in the show-line etc., but until that day arrives I can only recommend that you apply a vegetable oil, and that it is thoroughly removed with a wire brush afterwards. Nothing looks nicer than clean, sound, uncracked, balanced feet without any form of aesthetic dressing applied. Pony Clubs etc., please take note!

When looking after your horse's feet on a day to day basis, just ensure that the hoof is clean and that there is a nice clean groove down each side of the frog. Sometimes a horse will have a very shabby looking frog. This is because the frog is being constantly replaced and if the horse is not doing much work, then this can tend to come away in large lumps. The sole will often do the same. Neither of these things need worry you and besides I am sure the Farrier will keep the feet tidy.

By all means read all the advertisements for all the preparations on the market, but please ask one of the professionals in your team before using any of them.

───10───
Studs

I have a very definite view on studs; *screw-in studs should never be necessary in a horse shoe!* We have reached the stage where equine courses are having to be built bigger, longer, faster and more complex in order to extract a winner and to please an insatiable public and media. This cannot be the corect trend to follow as, eventually, the only outcome will be damage caused to the animal. We are all well aware of the gruesome tales of horses having to be put down at one event or another.

The action of screwing in studs does not necessarily make the horse feel any safer, it simply gives the rider a misplaced sense of confidence to push the horse to the extremes they believe the studs will allow.

The very principle of a stud being effective, means that the horse is having to cope with the extra jarring to its whole system as it tries to absorb the increased effects of concussion. There are times when the professional rider believes that this is a price worth paying, and I am sure this subjective point of view will continue the argument for and against for a very long time to come. However, I do wish that the average amateur rider would think carefully about what is actually happening to the horse when studs are fitted, and the consequences of this action.

First it is important to realise the imbalance that is being caused by fitting studs.

If one stud is fitted to each shoe, then at the stance, the horse will be thrown away from the stud. Before using the argument that the stud sinks into the ground, bear in mind that *if* it is going to do its job effectively it *has* to throw the animal out of balance. If two studs are fitted to each shoe then the horse will be tipped forward at the stance, and substantial extra jarring (albeit even) will be incurred upon landing.

I will not fit screw stud holes to shoes.

I would much rather that we began to consider the going conditions that prevail on the day and whether the individual horse is up to the job being asked of it, rather than fitting a larger stud just because it has been raining.

This, I admit, may be the view of a purist but, since the fitting of jumping studs effects a small minority of the equine world, it is a view I can afford to take.

Fig 37 – Heel Studs

This diagram illustrates the straining effect that studs (a) fitted to the heels of a shoe (b) can cause. The first point of damage is to the coronary band directly above the stud where, due to the uneven pressure, the horn tissue is shunted upwards. This strain then continues from the dorsal wall on up to the leg affecting the pastern, fetlock, knee, shoulder and back. (d) (e)

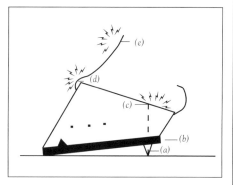

Fig 38 – One Stud

This is what happens when a horse stands on a hard surfacewith one stud (b) in the shoe (a).
The initial impact travels up to the coronary band (d) which causes a strain on the opposite wall area (c). This shock wave is then transmitted up the leg in alternate medial,lateral strains.

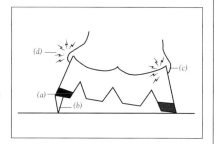

Fig 39 – Grip Effect

This diagram shows the shoe with the stud digging in the ground (a). If the going conditions impede the action of the horse it is important to know the the effect the use of studs will have on the horse's foot, and where the force inside the foot (b) is absorbed.
Primarily, it is absorbed at the laminae attachment in the dorsal area, except when the horse is turning, when it will be more on the lateral or medial attachment.

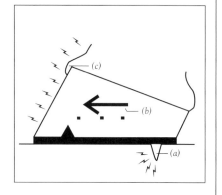

The Horse's Foot and Related Problems

──11──
Competition Shoeing

T here are a number of Farriers within the profession who like to take part in shoeing competitions. This is when Farriers compete against each other, usually at Agricultural Shows or Equine events, demonstrating the various disciplines of shoeing upon live animals in front of the public.

I cannot think of any other profession, registered under the Animal Welfare Act, where individuals go on public display and compete against each other. Competition shoeing is one of the worst traditions that the profession of Farriery has sadly decided to preserve. Despite the fact that you can undoubtedly see some very fine anvil skills at these events, it has turned the profession into a spectator sport without fully being aware of the consequences.

Until I see Vets taking part in, for example, a castration competition, and under the same parameters as Farriers, i.e. within a strict time limit, and under conditions set by the organisers of the show, then I fail to see the relevance of competition shoeing.

The shoeing performed at these events is usually under the instruction of the judges, who also set the tasks of each of the disciplines that the horse is to be shod for. In most competitions *one* Farrier will shoe *one* foot in each class. Thus a horse being used at one of these events could be shod by up to *four* different Farriers. Sometimes the *highest placed* Farrier will put on one front shoe and the *lowest placed* Farrier the other, strongly suggesting that the horse could be left distinctly unbalanced.

Perhaps the saddest aspect of the whole procedure is that the viewing public will automatically assume the winner of the competition to be the good Farrier, and although this could be correct, the result is reached more by accident than design. To be a *good* Farrier you must be able to understand how a horse works, and to make the horse you are presented with as balanced and bio-mechanically efficient as possible.

Farriers who wish to take the profession forward are being held back by the dogma of traditional values, such as competition shoeing.

The only competition that should exist is the one between knowledge and the unbalanced animal.

The Horse's Foot and Related Problems

——12——
Diet

I am not a qualified dietician, and have no intention of writing a section on what your horse should or should not be eating in terms of individual feeds. This I believe should be done by a professional. On the other hand I am often at the receiving end of badly fed horses which can manifest itself in anything from laminitis to animals that are simply 'hyped up' because their energy intake is not being adequately used up, and consequently the animal is too unruly to be safely attended.

I beg owners to get back to understanding just how a horse and its digestive system works. The horse evolved as an animal who roams arid plains constantly searching for grass and eating for 18 hours out of every 24. It's energy requirements are:-

a: to just survive, b: to breed, and c: to avoid predators.

It is this latter form of energy requirement that I believe the modern horse is now being fed for, i.e. the quick recall energy, as in flight. For a lot of performing horses this may well be alright but it is becoming the norm for the average hack, show horse, horse at rest, child's pony etc., where there is no requirement for this type of energy release except in very small amounts, and then, only if the animal is being adequately worked.

So, how do you ensure that your horse-at-rest maintains good condition, BUT DOES NOT GET FAT? First, accept the fact that your horse needs to have a diet made up mainly of fibre, and that it will function much better if the fibre it is given bears a close resemblance to the natural food that the animal would have access to in the wild. Today it is very easy to obtain food that is based on fibre, but much of it is so palatable that it is eaten too quickly, leaving the horse hours with nothing to do, resulting in bad stable habits or standing around the field gate waiting for its next food injection!

Feeding off the floor is much better for the animal than from a manger or hay rack as the breathing mechanism finds it easier to resist seeds and husks when in the natural 'head down' position.

In the section on laminitis you will see I mentioned that certain types of hay are passive and non-inflammatory. This is a good medium for getting fibre into the animal because it will take longer to eat than most foods. If you find that your horse is eating it's hay too fast then mix it with some clean oat straw to give it some bulk and thus make it last longer. There is only one type of hay for a horse and that is the *right hay*, and there is certainly no point in SOAKING the *wrong hay*.

I am often asked how and where to get good hay and my answer is always the same. Go to the farmer when the hay is still growing and ask if he will make it the way you want. This way the farmer is assured of a sale, and, the proverbial weather permitting, you get the right hay for your animal, plus the fact that it is a good idea to see your hay before it is cut in order to identify the various grass types that it contains.

Cereal foods have a part to play, so if you find that your horse is in need of more soluble energy, then cereals are a very natural and efficient way of getting this energy into the system. But it is so important that we start reducing the number of laminitics and animals with obesity related problems which sadly seem to be forever on the increase. So many of these problems are due to the over feeding of this type of soluble energy food.

When a horse is admitted to the Clinic and we have to consider a suitable diet, we must take into account the fact that the animal will not have access to a field and is therefore deprived of many if its trace elements, minerals and vitamins. To this end I use a diet that is suitable for all horses whether a youngster or an old laminitic. It works by carefully weighing out the amount of food to be given and then monitoring the animal. Do bear in mind that I am aiming for a passive animal, and that the animal will not be working. The diet is made up from the following:-

Sugar-beet: for easily digestible energy (from the sugar)
bran: for protein } both in very
oats: for starch, energy and fibre } small amounts
limestone flour, kelp, molasses, cod-liver oil, clean earth (mole hills are good for this)
organic, late, first cut hay, and *fresh spring water*: ad lib

Fig 37 shows the internal workings of the digestive system of the horse. Note how small the stomach is in relation to the rest of the digestive system. The large rear gut should be dealing with the slow extraction of energy from the courser foods, and it is this process that helps to achieve a passive animal. Any food passing through the gut of a normal healthy horse has a recognised pace of approximately 62 hours

The Horse's Foot and Related Problems

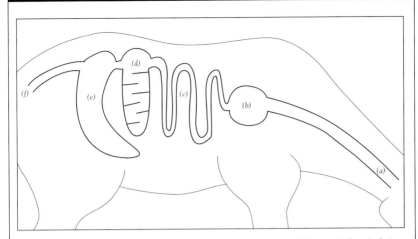

Fig 40 – The Horse's Gut

a) Oesophagus b) Stomach c) Small Intestine d) Caecum e) Large & Small Colon f) Rectum.

Food enters the mouth and travels down the oesophagus to the stomach (which is far smaller than most owners think!). It then passes through the small intestine, which is approximately 72 feet in length, and proceeds to the rear gut, which consists of the caecum and the small and large colon. Finally it is passed out through the rectum. The whole processs should take approximately 62 hours to complete. You will notice just how small the stomach is when compared to the rest of the gut and, hence, just how dangerous it is to OVERFEED.

from input to exit. If this process is speeded up then it is more than likely that the rear gut will end up containing food it is not designed to cope with. This food now in the rear gut greatly increases the chances of various problems arising, not least laminitis. This process is just as likely to happen to horses or ponies, thin or fat.

This 'speeding up' of the passage of food can be brought about by a number of things. As I have already mentioned in the chapter on Laminitis for the owner, stress seems to be an important factor in this process and I further mention that there is a distinction between stress and distress.

I would urge owners to visualise their horses as animals that are happiest when they are allowed to function at their optimum. In other words animals that are able to use to the best of their ability the three types of energy that I mentioned at the start of this chapter. Stud owners should be aware that it is harder to breed from an obese animal than one that is balanced. At Greatcombe Clinic we are also finding that joint problems in youngsters are far more common in those whose dams were overfed.

The general rule to be applied is to first work out a good base diet, and then add to it the extra energy you need to provide, and in what form you want to use it. i.e.

a) basic survival, e.g. a pony that is used only now and then.

b) breeding. Only enough to keep the mare balanced.

c) The need for high performance e.g. competition horses who require quick release energy in the form of food that will be digested in the early part of the gut. Please do not ignore the rear gut requirements in these horses.

Here are some approximate examples of Digestible Energy (D.E.), Crude Protein (C.P.) in some equine foods. The energy is measured in megajoules per kilogram. (Mj/Kg)

FOOD	D.E. mj/kg	C.P. %
Sugar-beet	12 to 13	7 to 8
Barley	13 to 15	10 to 11
Oats	13 to 15	10 to 12
Bran	10 to 12	16 to 18
Carrots	11 to 13	8 to 10
GRASSES		
Rye grass	7 to 9	10 to 12
Clover	7 to 9	17 to 19
Lucerne	7 to 9	18 to 20
HAYS		
Well made clover	7 to 9	15 to 17
Late cut organic	4 to 7	5 to 8
STRAWS		
Barley	5 to 7	3 to 5
Oat	5 to 7	3 to 5

The bran is always fed with limestone flour which is 39.4% calcium, because bran tends to create a need for calcium. I only use late cut organic hay which I feed ad lib, using the other foods to control condition.

Feeding a horse should be fun. Please remember that from the horse's point of view it is the best part of the day, and that he will eat almost anything when he is hungry enough, whether it is good for him or not. Don't be afraid to let the horse's weight fluctuate a little with the seasons. If he were on the plains this would be only natural, and by losing a little weight (but not condition) towards the end of the winter, he is more able to tolerate the influx of extra nutrients and added energy sugars in the spring grass.

Most importantly the horse looks to you for all the requirements that he would find in the wild, and you have to be particularly vigilant since most equine food preparations today mean that everyday is springtime!

The Horse's Foot and Related Problems

──13──
The Law

The law which covers the shoeing of horses in this country (at the time of this book going to print,) is quite clear; you must be registered with the Farriers Registration Council (F.R.C.) before you are allowed to practice the profession of Farriery. The F.R.C. has to comply with the Animal Welfare Act which states that:-

Only Qualified Veterinary Surgeons can diagnose, form a prognosis or treat an animal.

There are two exceptions:
1) The rendering of first-aid for saving life and relieving pain.
2) Any treatment given to an animal by its owner, a member of his household or his employee.

Although I have heard it said many times that a Farrier knows more about the feet of a horse than a Vet, it must be pointed out that unless the Farrier obtains the permission of the Vet, any subsequent surgical work carried out on the animal could be deemed to be illegal! This restriction is welcomed by all good Farriers as it prevents work being carried out on a horse which deprives the owner of redress against the perpetrator. It is possible for a Farrier to be removed from the Register. A complaint would have to be lodged with the F.R.C., an investigation would then take place and the offender would go before a disciplinary committee.

If you need to know more about the Council, further information may be obtained from the following address.

The Registrar, Farriers Registration Council,
P.O. Box 49, East of England Show Ground,
Peterborough, PE2 6GU
Tel: 0733 371171

The Registration of Farriers is set out in four parts.
Part 1 Farriers who have passed the correct examinations. R.S.S. DIP WCF, Army B2 test or similar test that satisfies the F.R.C.

Part 2 Farriers that had been in the business of shoeing horses without the relevant qualifications for at least two years before the register started.

Part 3 People who shoe their own horses.

Part 4 Farriers who have done a apprenticeship but have not taken the examination.

Entry to parts 2,3 and 4 ceased after June 30th 1980 (with the exception of late applications especially permitted by the council under section 7)

The Worshipful Company of Farriers have three examinations in Farriery:-

1) The Diploma - dip WCF - this exam, or something similar, has to be passed in order to be registered as a Farrier.

2) The Associate - AWCF - this exam has to be taken before you can take your Fellowship exam.

3) Fellowship - FWCF - this is the highest exam possible in the Worshipful Company of Farriers.

Neither of these last two exams, although intense, make the successful candidate any more qualified than the first exam as far as the Animal Welfare Act is concerned. They are for internal recognition only.

Owners must be aware that they also come under the Animal Welfare Act which is enforced by the R.S.P.C.A. and if any member of the public believes that an animal is being abused, then they should contact the R.S.P.C.A..

At the end of the day, the law is there to protect the animal, but it is always a good idea to prevent a situation deteriorating to the extent where the law is needed.

Laws are created for extremes.

The Veterinary profession is represented by the:-
Royal College of Veterinary Surgeons,
Royal College Street,
London NW1 0TU
Tel: 071 387 2898